THE GREAT GAMES BOOK

Susan Adams

DORLING KINDERSLEY
London • New York • Moscow • Sydney

A Dorling Kindersley Book

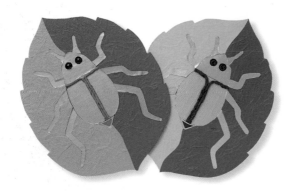

Editor   Victoria Edgley
Art Editor   Cheryl Telfer
Photographer   Steve Gorton

Managing Editor   Jane Yorke
Managing Art Editor   Chris Scollen
Production   Josie Alabaster
DTP Designer   Almudena Díaz
Picture Researcher   Thomas Worsley

First published in Great Britain in 1997
by Dorling Kindersley Limited
9 Henrietta Street, London WC2E 8PS

ISBN: 0-7513-5672-7

Colour reproduction by Bright Arts, Hong Kong
Printed and bound in Italy by A. Montadori Editore, Verona

Picture credits: Tony Stone Images: 13tr, 27tr, Keren Su 11crb, Glen Allison
7crb, S&N Geary 32cb, Renee Lynn 35cr, Herb Schmitz 13br. Planet Earth
Pictures: 46bl, 41cr. Rex Features: 29cr. Hutchison: 23tr, 34tl, S. Errington
36br. Panos Pictures: 32bl. Robert Harding Picture Library: 21crb.
Additional photography: Dave King 6tl, British Museum
C Graham/N Nicholls 18cl, B&A Kindersley 25br,
Colin Keates 39br, Jerry Young 42bl, Steve Shott 42tl, Susanna Price 44br.

Dorling Kindersley would like to thank Mark Haygarth
for jacket design, Anne-Marie Ryan for editorial assistance, and
Sarah Cowley, Jackie Gooden, Jo Malivoire, and Dean Price for design
assistance. Dorling Kindersley would also like to thank the following
models for appearing in this book: Thomas Brightman, Scott Dennis,
Duran Earle, Collette Haydon, Connie Kirkby, Taskin Kuyucuoglu,
Tolga Kuyucuoglu, Scott Lamb, Johnathan Lawrence, Gemma Loke,
Johnathan McInyre, Lian Ng, Jade Ogugua, Natasha Payne, Kirsty Thomas,
Natasha Trinnamen, and Chloe Whitmarsh.

CONTENTS

INTRODUCTION

This book is packed with exciting games from around the world for you to make and play. Below you can see some useful things to collect to make the game pieces. Before you start to play each game, make sure you read through the instructions and are familiar with the scoring. When you have finished playing, remember to put everything away and clean up any mess you have made.

Things to collect

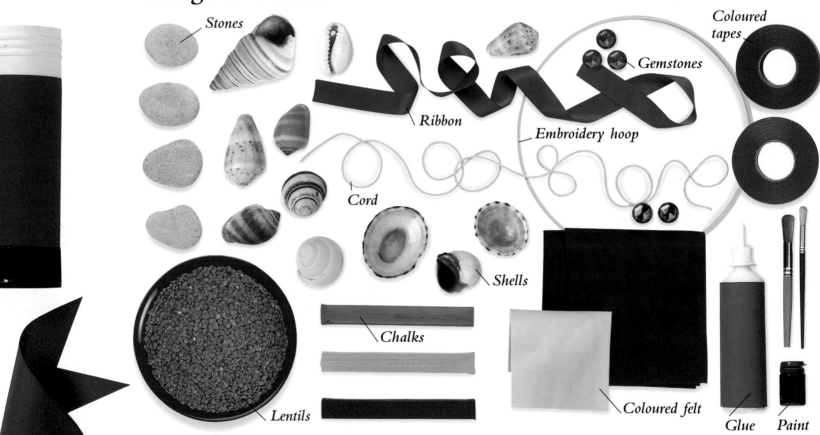

Stones

Coloured tapes

Gemstones

Ribbon

Embroidery hoop

Cord

Shells

Chalks

Coloured felt

Lentils

Glue   Paint

Nature collection

Collect any useful or interesting natural objects to use as game pieces. Small shells, pebbles, and stones are all used in this book.

Craft materials

Craft materials and equipment are needed to make some of the games. Gather together glue, ribbon, paper, card, paints, brushes, and felt and store them in a safe place.

Warning symbols

Look out for the red warning signs in the step-by-step instructions of some projects.

The warning symbol
You will see this sign when sharp tools are used. Always ask an adult to help you.

Star times

At the top of each page you will find a star symbol that tells you how long the game pieces will take to make.

One star
☆ Project takes an hour or less to complete.

Two stars
☆ ☆ Project takes an afternoon to complete.

Three stars
☆ ☆ ☆ Project takes a day or more to complete.

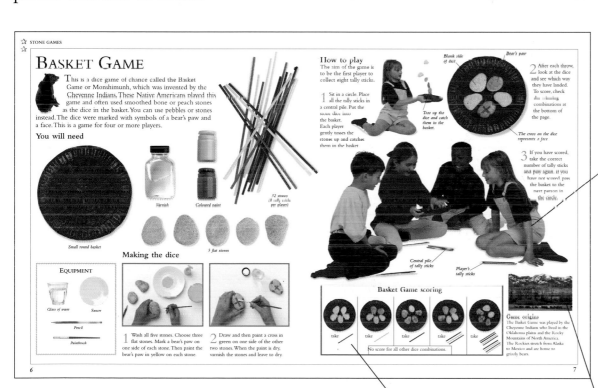

How to play
The rules for each game are explained with clear photographs and simple step-by-step instructions.

Step-by-step instructions

Each double page shows exactly what you will need to make the game pieces and boards. Simple step-by-steps show you how to play each game.

Score box
These boxes show players how to score and win the game.

Game origins
Colour photographs and captions explain which country the game has come from, or provide an interesting fact about the game.

BASKET GAME

This is a dice game of chance called the Basket Game or Monshimunh, which was invented by the Cheyenne Indians. These Native Americans played this game and often used smoothed bone or peach stones as the dice in the basket. You can use pebbles or stones instead. The dice were marked with symbols of a bear's paw and a face. This is a game for four or more players.

You will need

Varnish

Coloured paint

*32 straws
(8 tally sticks
per player)*

Small round basket

5 flat stones

Making the dice

EQUIPMENT

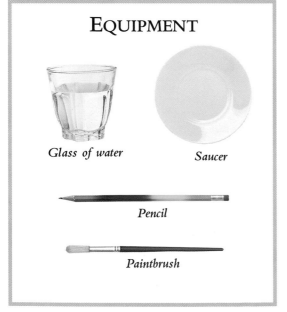

Glass of water

Saucer

Pencil

Paintbrush

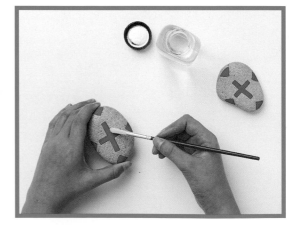

1 Wash all five stones. Choose three flat stones. Mark a bear's paw on one side of each stone. Then paint the bear's paw in yellow on each stone.

2 Draw and then paint a cross in green on one side of the other two stones. When the paint is dry, varnish the stones and leave to dry.

How to play

The aim of the game is to be the first player to collect eight tally sticks.

1 Sit in a circle. Place all the tally sticks in a central pile. Put the stone dice into the basket. Each player gently tosses the stones up and catches them in the basket.

Toss up the dice and catch them in the basket.

Blank side of dice

Bear's paw

2 After each throw, look at the dice and see which way they have landed. To score, check the winning combinations at the bottom of the page.

The cross on the dice represents a face.

3 If you have scored, take the correct number of tally sticks and play again. If you have not scored, pass the basket to the next person in the circle.

Central pile of tally sticks

Player's tally sticks

Basket Game scoring

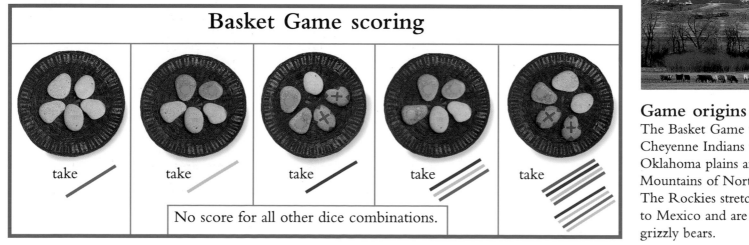

take	take	take	take	take

No score for all other dice combinations.

Game origins

The Basket Game was played by the Cheyenne Indians who lived in the Oklahoma plains and the Rocky Mountains of North America. The Rockies stretch from Alaska to Mexico and are home to grizzly bears.

FIVE STONE JACKS

Games with Jacks are played in countries all over the world. Traditionally, players used the knucklebones of sheep for playing pieces. In India, children play a version of Jacks called Pacheta. Since India is a hot country, Pacheta is played outside on dry ground using small stones. This is a game for two or more players.

Making the pieces

1 Choose five small stones and clean them. Carefully mark a shape on each stone and then paint them in different colours as shown.

2 Carefully varnish each stone to protect the paint on the stones. Leave the stones to dry fully before using them in the game.

You will need

Coloured paint

Varnish

EQUIPMENT

Paintbrush

Saucer

Pencil

Glass of water

5 small flat stones

SHELL GAME

This is a game using shells called Izingendo, which Zulu children in South Africa play. It is an ideal game for the beach for two players.

1 Dig a hole in the sand. Put five shells in the hole and throw a shell in the air. Using the same hand, try to scoop all the shells out of the hole, and catch the thrown shell.

Scoop the shells out of the hole.

You will need

20 small shells

How to play

1 Take all five stones in the palm of your hand. With your hand in front of you, throw the stones up about 15 cm in the air.

2 As the stones are coming down, try to catch them on the back of your hand. Keep your fingers together so that the stones don't slip through.

3 Throw the stones from the back of your hand into your palm. The player who has caught the most stones starts the game.

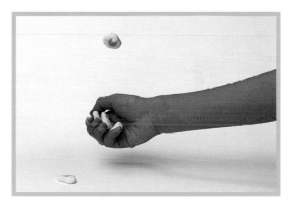

4 Scatter the stones on the ground. Throw one stone in the air, pick up a stone from the ground and catch the thrown stone with the same hand.

5 Repeat until you have picked up all the stones. Then scatter the stones, throw one in the air and pick up the remaining stones in pairs.

6 Then pick up three stones, and four stones. If you miss, the other player has a go. You start from where you finished when you have a new turn.

2 If you don't catch the thrown shell, or leave some shells in the hole, the turn passes to the next player. Add an extra shell to the hole after each round.

7 Make an arch with your forefinger and thumb. Scatter the stones, throw one up and tap one stone through the arch. Repeat for each stone. Then do pairs, threes, and fours.

To finish the game, throw up a stone and scoop up the other stones.

SPILLIKINS

This is a game for steady hands that comes from China. In the past, players used delicate ivory or thin wooden sticks painted with bands of colour. The sticks were also used for fortune telling. You can use skewers instead of sticks in this game for two or more players.

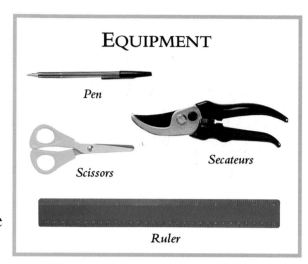

EQUIPMENT

Pen

Scissors

Secateurs

Ruler

Ribbon tied tightly in a bow.

Finished Spillikins

When you have finished playing the game, tie a ribbon around the spillikins to store them.

You will need

Red and blue tape

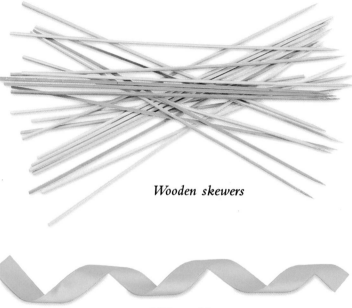

Wooden skewers

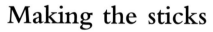

Yellow ribbon

Making the sticks

1 Measure and mark 30 skewers to make them all the same length. Ask an adult to trim the points off the skewers by using the secateurs.

2 Cut some short lengths of red and blue tape. Wind these around the sticks, using the list opposite as a guide where to place the tape.

Make up the following sticks:

6 skewers with one red band

6 skewers with two red bands

2 skewers with three red bands

2 skewers with two red and blue bands

6 skewers with one blue band

6 skewers with two blue bands

2 skewers with three blue bands

How to play

The aim of the game is to remove as many sticks from the central pile as you can, without moving any other stick.

1 Players sit in a circle. One player holds the spillikins and rests the ends on a table or the floor.

2 Let the spillikins go so that they fall in a jumbled heap. Each player takes a turn in carefully removing a stick from the central pile.

Trim the ribbon so that it doesn't fray.

3 If a player manages to remove a stick without moving others in the pile, then he or she keeps the stick and has another go. If the player moves another stick, then the next player has a turn.

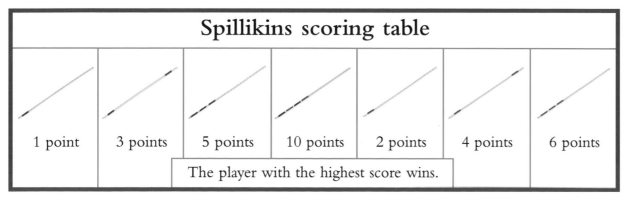

4 When all the sticks have been taken, players check their scores using the table below to find the winner.

Player's pile of sticks

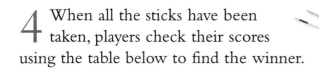

Spillikins scoring table

1 point	3 points	5 points	10 points	2 points	4 points	6 points

The player with the highest score wins.

Game origins
Spillikins was traditionally played by the emperors of Ancient China. During the Ming Dynasty, an emperor built a palace in Beijing called the Forbidden City.

PAPER, SCISSORS, STONE

This is a fast-moving hand game from Japan originally called Jan Ken Pon, meaning paper, sword, fist. The aim of this game for two is for each player to beat the other in a quick show of hands.

How to play

A clenched fist represents a stone.

Two fingers represent scissors.

A flat hand represents paper.

Scoring

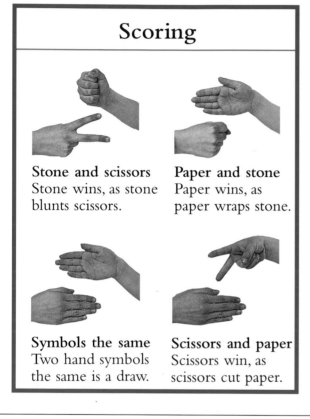

Stone and scissors
Stone wins, as stone blunts scissors.

Paper and stone
Paper wins, as paper wraps stone.

Symbols the same
Two hand symbols the same is a draw.

Scissors and paper
Scissors win, as scissors cut paper.

1 Two players sit opposite each other. Both players clench a fist and chant Jan Ken Pon. On the word Pon, both players display a hand in one of the three positions shown above.

A clenched fist represents a stone.

In this case, paper wraps stone and wins this round.

THE WARRIOR GAME

This is a game that comes from New Zealand called Hei Tama Tu Tama. It is a game for two players who must move quickly in order to win the game.

How to play

1 Two players stand with their hands on their hips. One is the defender and calls out One Hei Tama Tu Tama. On the last word, both players display one of the four arm positions shown below.

Arm positions

Hand positions

Finger pointing to the left

Finger pointing straight down

Finger pointing to the right

Finger pointing straight up

Game origins
Intricate designs made with paper and scissors are part of Japan's ancient culture and the art of origami paper folding originated here. Japanese children still dress up in the traditional costume called the Kimono for special occasions.

2 The winning player chants Atchi Muiti Hoi and points a finger in one direction. At the same time, the other player must move his or her head, trying to avoid the same direction as the winner.

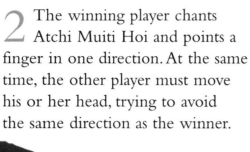

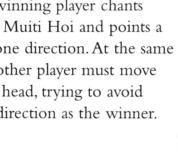

If the hand and the head positions mirror each other, then the player pointing wins.

If the hand and head positions are different, then the round is a draw.

Head positions

Head up

Head to the left

Head to the right

Head down

2 If both players choose the same position, the defender wins a point and continues calling. If they choose different positions, neither scores and the challenger calls the next round.

A point can only be scored by the defender calling the round.

Scoring
After winning a point, the player starts the next round by calling out Two Hei Tama Tu Tama. The first player to reach Ten Hei Tama Tu Tama wins the game. The scoring moves on only when a point is won.

Game origins
The Maoris from New Zealand thought that hand and arm games were good practice for warriors, helping them develop quick reactions.

HOOP AND DART

Native Americans played many games to improve their hunting skills. Hoop and Dart was invented to practise throwing spears. This version for two people can be played on any smooth area of ground.

Making the hoop

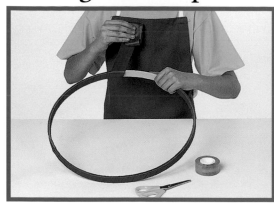

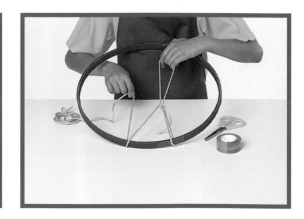

1 Tape one end of the ribbon to the hoop. Wrap the ribbon around the hoop, making sure it overlaps so it is covered. Secure the ribbon with tape.

2 Make a loop with one end of the cord. With the remaining cord, thread it around the hoop and then back through the cord loop.

You will need

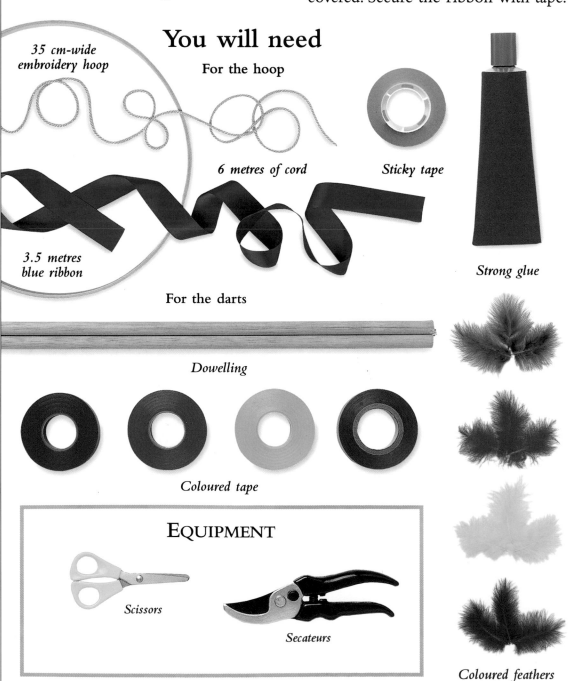

35 cm-wide embroidery hoop

For the hoop

6 metres of cord

Sticky tape

3.5 metres blue ribbon

Strong glue

For the darts

Dowelling

Coloured tape

Coloured feathers

EQUIPMENT

Scissors

Secateurs

Making the darts

1 Ask an adult to cut four pieces of dowelling 20 cm long with the secateurs. Put two feathers on some tape and wrap around the end of the stick.

2 Decorate the stick with coloured tape. Wrap coloured tape around the end opposite the feathers. Now make three more feathered darts.

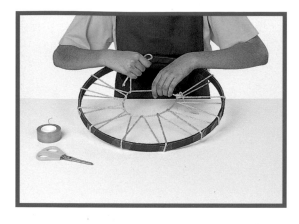

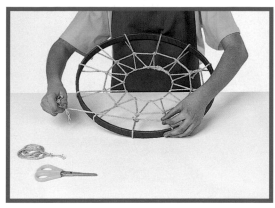

3 Repeat this process until you have gone around the entire hoop. Tape the cord spokes to the hoop. To finish, tie the cord to the hoop.

4 Weave a piece of cord around the spokes, tying it securely at every intersection. Repeat with another piece of cord to form a web.

5 At each intersection, glue the cord knots together to keep them securely in place. Leave the hoop to dry thoroughly before using it.

How to play

One player takes the hoop, and the other player takes the darts. The first player rolls the hoop along the ground while the second player tries to shoot the darts through the centre of the hoop. Players score as shown below.

Dreamcatchers were hung above the sleeping area.

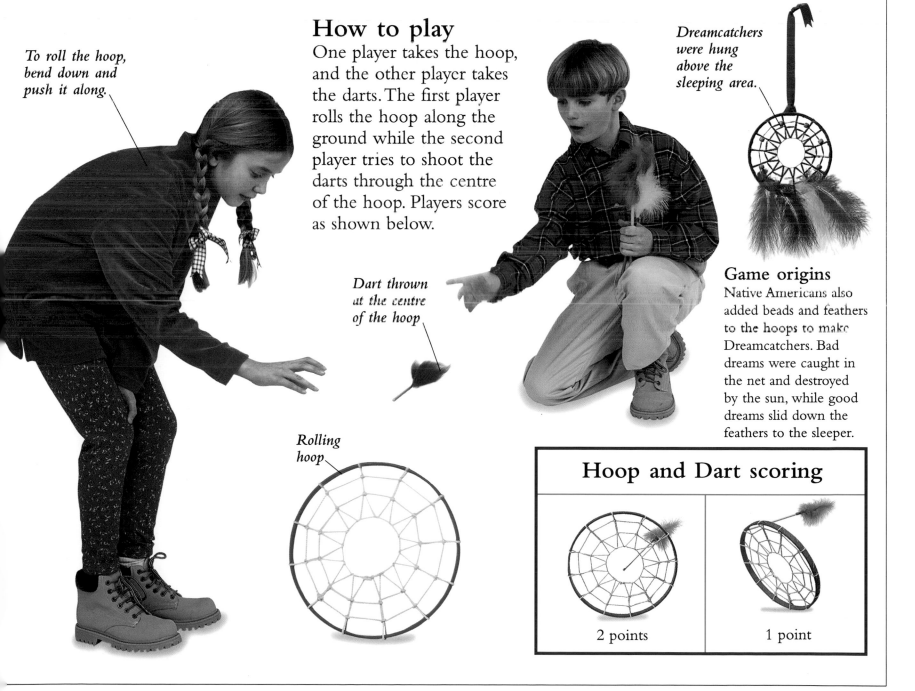

To roll the hoop, bend down and push it along.

Dart thrown at the centre of the hoop

Rolling hoop

Game origins

Native Americans also added beads and feathers to the hoops to make Dreamcatchers. Bad dreams were caught in the net and destroyed by the sun, while good dreams slid down the feathers to the sleeper.

Hoop and Dart scoring

2 points	1 point

POLE GAMES

Here are two outdoor games from Brazil, using the same pole, and hoops and stones to throw. With practice, your throws will become more accurate.

You will need

For Hit it Off

Coloured tapes

EQUIPMENT

Scissors

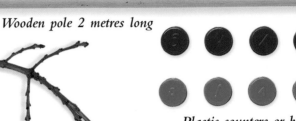

2 stones per player

For the Hoop Game

4 embroidery hoops 20 cm across

Coloured tape

Wooden pole 2 metres long

Twig or stick

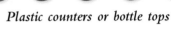

Plastic counters or bottle tops

Hit it Off

This game for two players relies on an accurate eye and careful aim. Make sure that both players stand on the same side of the circle so that neither player gets hit by a stone.

Decorating the pole

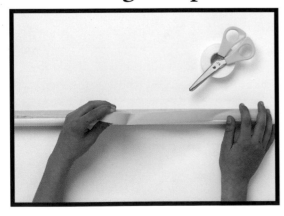

To decorate the pole, stick long strips of yellow and white tape down its length. Cover the whole pole to protect it from knocks and scratches.

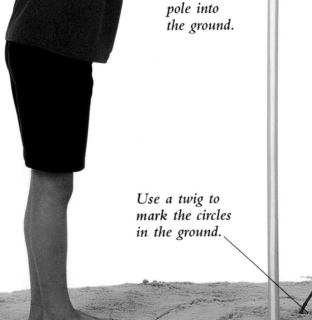

Push the pole into the ground.

Use a twig to mark the circles in the ground.

How to play

1 Hammer the pole into the ground. Balance a counter or bottle top on the top of the pole. Mark two circles round the pole, one 50 cm away and another 1 metre away.

The Hoop Game

This is a game for two or more players.
Throw a hoop over a pole to score points.

Decorating the hoops

Use the inside rings of four
embroidery hoops. Completely cover
two hoops in blue tape, and two
hoops in red, as shown.

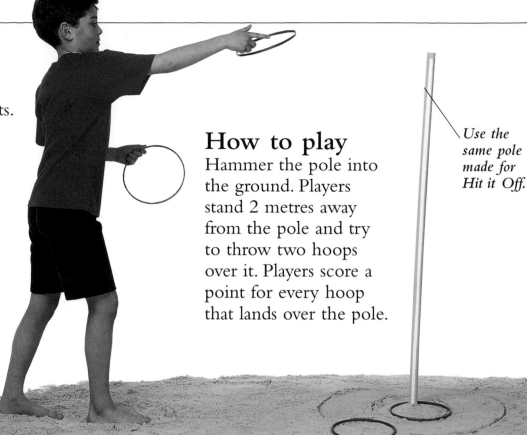

How to play

Hammer the pole into
the ground. Players
stand 2 metres away
from the pole and try
to throw two hoops
over it. Players score a
point for every hoop
that lands over the pole.

*Use the
same pole
made for
Hit it Off.*

*Aim the stone at the top
of the pole and try to
knock off the counter.*

2 Players stand away from
the outer circle and take
turns throwing a stone to try
and knock the counter off the
pole. If the counter falls into
the inner circle, the player
scores one point. If the counter
falls into the outer circle, the
player scores two points.

Placing the counter
Each time a counter falls,
replace it by carefully
positioning another on
the top of the pole.

Winning the game
The winner is the player
with the highest total of
points after an agreed
number of throws.

MARBLE GAMES

Glass marbles were very popular in Victorian England. Players competed in games to win marbles from each other. Here is a collection of traditional marble games for two or more players.

Marble Pyramid

Marble games are sometimes played on the pavement sprinkled with dirt or damp sand. Players can use chalk to draw a circle directly on to the ground or smooth paved area.

You will need

Coloured chalk

Marble pyramid

A bag of marbles

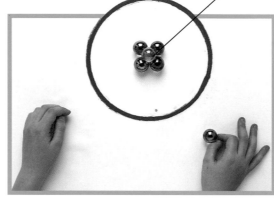

1 Draw a big circle with chalk. One player is keeper and makes a five marble pyramid in the circle, charging the other players one marble per turn.

2 The other players take turns in shooting a marble at the pyramid from 1 metre away. Each player keeps any marbles knocked out of the circle.

3 Marbles remaining inside the circle remain the property of the keeper. The keeper must rebuild the pyramid after each player's turn.

Bounce Eye

In Bounce Eye, players knock the marbles out of a circle by dropping a marble from eye height.

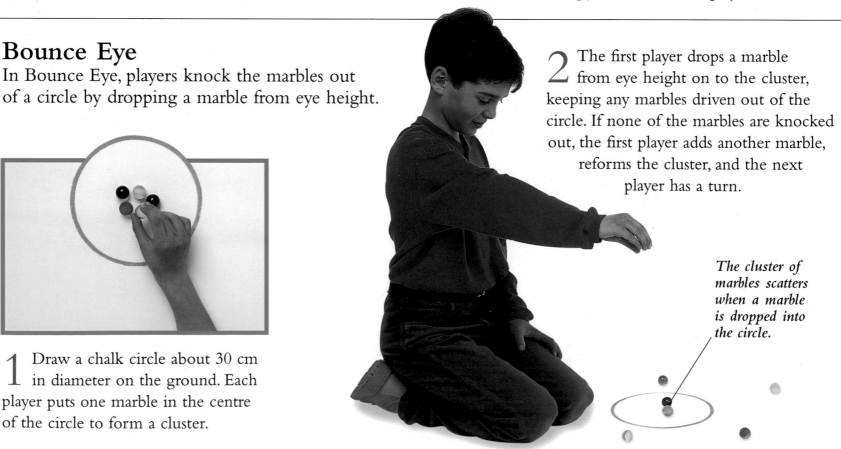

2 The first player drops a marble from eye height on to the cluster, keeping any marbles driven out of the circle. If none of the marbles are knocked out, the first player adds another marble, reforms the cluster, and the next player has a turn.

The cluster of marbles scatters when a marble is dropped into the circle.

1 Draw a chalk circle about 30 cm in diameter on the ground. Each player puts one marble in the centre of the circle to form a cluster.

Hundreds

For this game, players need to practise flicking the marbles accurate distances to roll inside a circle target.

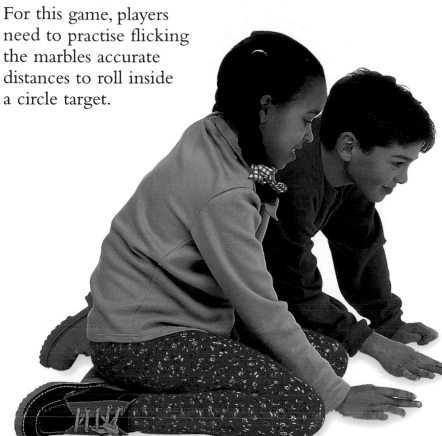

Flicking the marble with your forefinger

Flicking the marble with your thumb

How to play

Two players shoot a marble from behind a line drawn 3 metres from a chalk circle. In a round, if only one player's marble stops in the circle, this player scores 10 points. If both or neither of the marbles stop in the circle, both players shoot again.

The first player to score 100 points is the winner.

Picking Plums

This game for two players requires a steady aim. The marble used for shooting is often bigger than an ordinary marble and is called a taw or shooter. Retrieve the shooter after each turn.

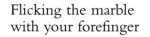

Game origins

Marbles games have been played throughout the centuries and appeared as early as Ancient Roman times. Roman children played games with marbles made of clay or glass.

How to play

Each player places two marbles in a straight line on the ground, 3 cms apart, to form a line of plums. Players take turns shooting from a second line 1.5 metres away, aiming to pick the plums, or hit the marbles. Players keep any marble they hit.

The line of plums, or marbles

Flicking a shooter

LIMBO

An energetic game for any number of players, Limbo can be played inside, outside, in the garden, or on a beach. Turn on some lively music and take turns in passing as low as possible under the bar!

Making the limbo bar

1 Ask an adult to measure and cut two bamboo poles, each 1 metre long. Cut ten rods, 5 cm long, and tape these 20 cm apart on the poles.

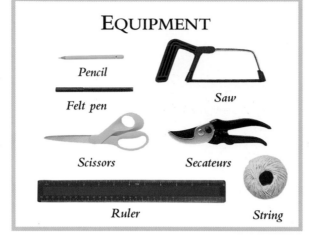

EQUIPMENT

Pencil

Felt pen

Saw

Scissors

Secateurs

Ruler

String

You will need

Coloured tapes

Modelling clay

Sticky tape

Card

Dowelling

Bamboo poles

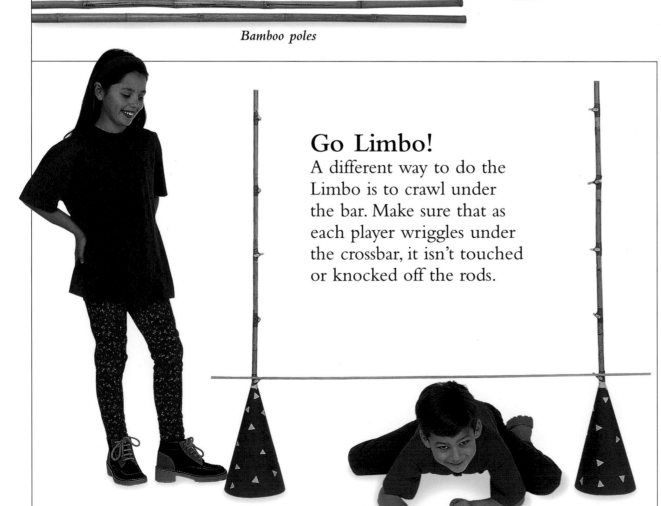

Go Limbo!

A different way to do the Limbo is to crawl under the bar. Make sure that as each player wriggles under the crossbar, it isn't touched or knocked off the rods.

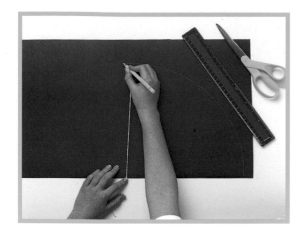

2 Cut out some card 50 cm x 25 cm. Using the pencil and the string, draw a semicircle on the card, as shown. Cut out the semicircle.

3 Carefully roll the cut-out card into a cone. Tape the join securely. Trim off the top of the cone, so that it will slip over the end of the pole.

4 Slip the cone over the bottom end of the pole. Tape the cone in place. Place some modelling clay on the end of the pole, to weigh it down.

How to play

The aim is for each player to take turns at passing under the bar, moving forwards but leaning over backwards.

To play the game, set up the poles and cones.

Bamboo crossbar

Make sure that you don't touch or knock the crossbar off the poles.

Cone decorated with coloured tape

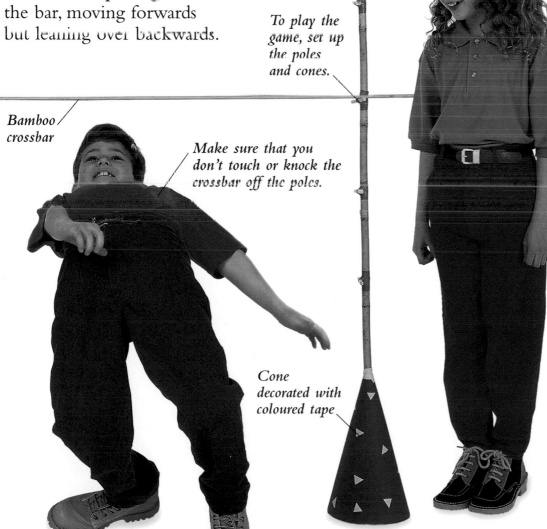

Moving the bar
When every player has passed under the crossbar, lower it another level. A player is out when he or she knocks the crossbar off the limbo stand.

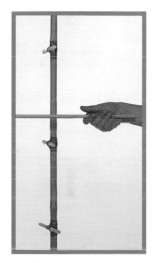

Game origins
Limbo dancing is a popular and traditional form of dance from the Caribbean Islands. Limbo dancers from the Caribbean can pass underneath a bar as low as 15 cm off the ground, displaying amazing levels of flexibility and balance.

KICK THE BIRD

Kick the Bird is an action game from Korea that is not as nasty as it sounds! The soft ball decorated like a bird can be made with any filling, from sawdust to lentils. Practice the different ways you can keep the bird off the ground without using your hands. Play this on your own or with a friend.

You will need

Coloured felt

Coloured sock

Lentils or beans

Strong glue

Spoon

Coloured feathers

EQUIPMENT

Scissors

Pen

Ruler

Making the bird

1 Ask an adult to hold a sock open for you and carefully fill it to the heel with the lentils to form a ball. Tie the sock firmly in a tight knot.

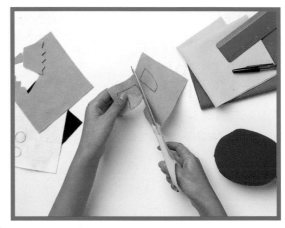

2 Cut two eyes and a beak out of felt. Glue these on to the sock to make a face. Cut out decorations for the sock tail and feet and glue them on.

3 Glue the ends of the coloured feathers before pushing them carefully into the sock for wings. Let the bird dry fully before using it.

The finished bird

The bird is a ball to kick with a face, tail, feet, and feathers.

Decorated sock end for a tail

Feathers pushed in to the sock for wings

Beak made from a double layer of felt

Game Origins

Korea is a country neighboured by China and Japan. Soldiers in Korea play this game as a means of making them quick witted. In cold weather children find it a good way of keeping their feet warm.

How to play

The aim of Kick the Bird is to keep the bird in the air for as long as possible without using your hands.

Between two players

Kick the bird between two players, seeing how long you can keep going before the bird falls.

Head butt

As the bird comes down, try hitting it with your forehead or the top of your head.

Knee kick

Drop the bird on to your knee and bounce it up in the air. Remember to keep your balance on your other leg.

Heel kick

Try to keep the bird off the ground by kicking it with the heel, front, or side of your foot.

SWING BALL

Ghana is a hot country on the west coast of Africa. Here children play Swing Ball, a game for two players, out of doors in the sun. The ball and rope also detach from the pole to become a jumping game for two or more people.

EQUIPMENT

Spoon

Scissors

Making the ball

You will need

For the ball

For the pole

2 wooden rings   *Coloured tape*

Strong glue   *1.5 metres of cord*

Thread

A pair of tights

Pole 2 metres long

250 g of lentils

1 Cut off one leg of the tights. Fill the toe with lentils. Tie it closed with thread before twisting the end and wrapping it back over the ball.

Jump Ball

Several players form a circle round one player who holds the rope and swings the ball round in a circle, 30 cms from the ground. When players are hit by the rope, they are out of the game.

Players jump the rope as it swings round in a circle.

Detach the rope from the pole

Making the pole

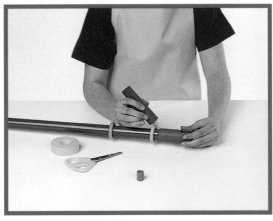

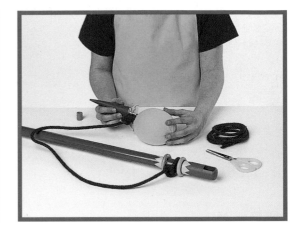

2 Now the soft ball has two outer layers to make it strong. To finish the ball, securely tie the open end with another length of thread.

1 Slide the two wooden rings on to the pole. Leave a 5 cm gap between the rings. Carefully glue them in place at the top of the pole.

2 Tie the cord securely to the ball. Tie the other end of the cord to the pole between the two wooden rings. Decorate the pole with tape.

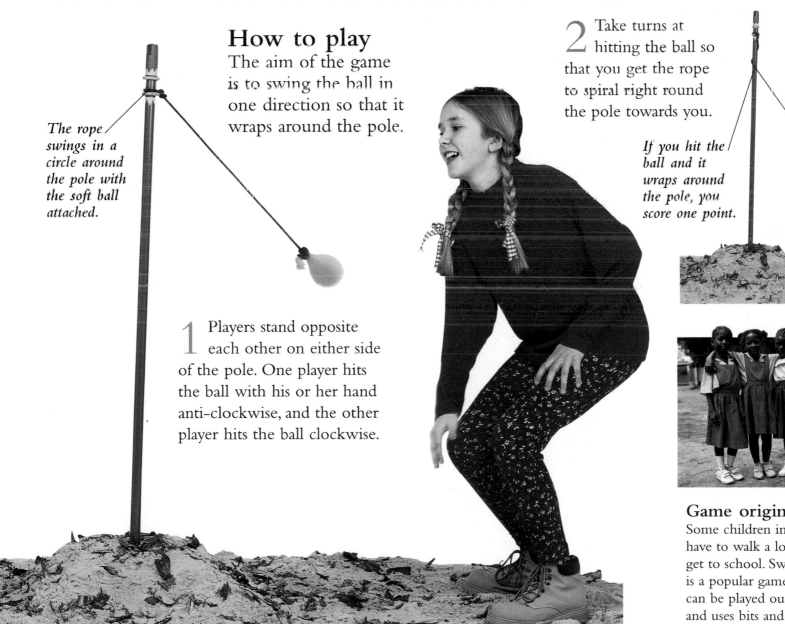

How to play
The aim of the game is to swing the ball in one direction so that it wraps around the pole.

The rope swings in a circle around the pole with the soft ball attached.

1 Players stand opposite each other on either side of the pole. One player hits the ball with his or her hand anti-clockwise, and the other player hits the ball clockwise.

2 Take turns at hitting the ball so that you get the rope to spiral right round the pole towards you.

If you hit the ball and it wraps around the pole, you score one point.

Game origins
Some children in Ghana have to walk a long way to get to school. Swing Ball is a popular game, as it can be played outside, and uses bits and pieces found in the home.

TUG OF WAR

Here is an Eskimo game for two players sitting on the ground. Tug of War games are a show of strength and often represent the struggle between two opposites such as good and evil, or hot and cold.

You will need

2 wooden poles 35 cm long

1.5 metres of rope

Coloured tape

Making the handles

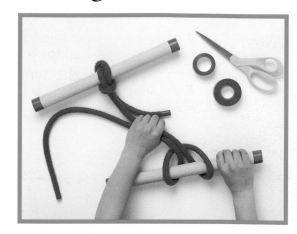

Decorate the ends of the handles with tape. Leaving 50 cm of rope between the handles, loop the rope around the handles and tie it in a knot.

GOLDEN GATE

This is a traditional game from the Czech Republic for six or more players, where good and evil do battle in a Tug of War.

The other players line up and pass under the gateway singing a rhyme.

1 Two players secretly choose to be either an angel or a devil. These players join hands and make an arch.

Lowered gate

2 When the gate is lowered, the trapped player chooses a side and stands beside the player. The next trapped player stands beside the opposite player. This continues until each player is on a team.

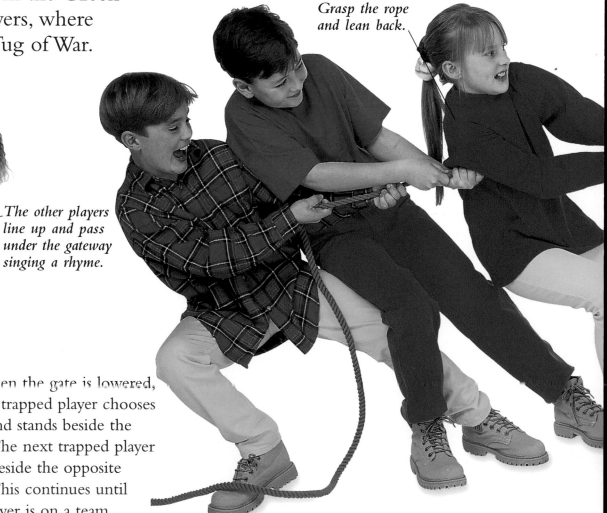

Grasp the rope and lean back.

How to play

Two players, roughly the same height, sit opposite each other with their feet touching. Each player grips a handle and pulls until the rope is taut. On the word "Go!", both players tug on the handles, trying to pull the other player over.

Keep your arms straight.

Grip the handles tightly.

Game origins

In Northern Canada, Tug of War is played to predict how cold winter will be. One team consists of people born in winter, the other of people born in summer – if summer wins, it will be a warm winter.

How to play

Each team, selected secretly for the good or the evil side, must have an equal number of players. The team that pulls the other team over the mark to their side wins the war.

Grip the rope with both hands.

3 Draw a mark on the ground. The angel and the devil then reveal their identity and the Tug of War begins. Each team takes hold of the rope and on the word "Go!", pulls hard, trying to get the other team to fall over the mark.

Line between the two teams.

Place your feet wide apart for a steady base.

SKIPPING

Children everywhere have skipped rope for centuries, often chanting rhymes as they skip. Start with forward and backward skipping before moving on to more complicated steps.

You will need

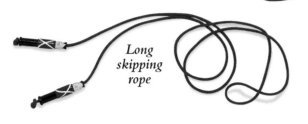

Long skipping rope

Short skipping rope

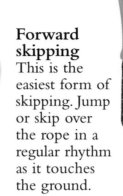

Swing the rope up over your head and down in front of you.

Hold one rope handle in each hand.

Forward skipping
This is the easiest form of skipping. Jump or skip over the rope in a regular rhythm as it touches the ground.

Backward skipping
Start with the rope in front of your feet. Swing it up in front of you and over your head.

Jump with your feet together.

Trick skipping

For single skipping, the ideal length of rope should stretch from one shoulder, under your feet and up to the other shoulder. Here are some fun skipping tricks to master.

Swing the rope to one side then the other, with a skip in-between.

Boxercise skipping
Complete one forward skip, then pass the rope to one side and swing it in a circle.

Cross your arms to make a loop to skip through

Cross-arm skipping
Start with a forward skip. Cross your arms in front of you as the rope comes over your head, and skip through the loop formed by the rope. Follow this with another forward step.

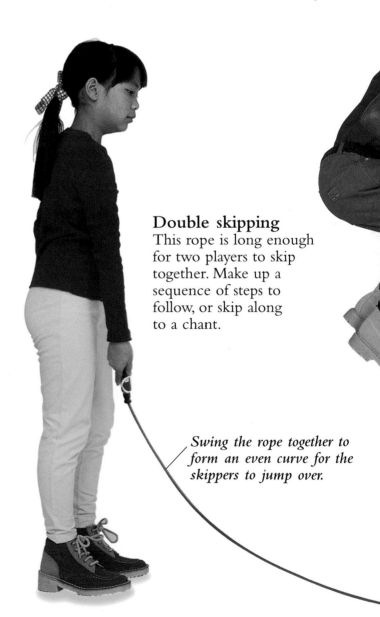

Double skipping
This rope is long enough for two players to skip together. Make up a sequence of steps to follow, or skip along to a chant.

Swing the rope together to form an even curve for the skippers to jump over.

Skipping in pairs
One player starts skipping. A second player jumps in to join the first player and they skip together.

Jump at the same time to allow the rope to keep moving.

One player skips backwards and the other player skips forwards.

Advanced skipping
Another way to skip in a pair, is to have one player turn one end of the rope and one player jump, as shown.

Turn the rope and jump at the same time.

Jump over the rope when it hits the ground.

Grip the rope with one hand.

Group skipping
Two players are the rope holders, and take one end of the rope and turn it continuously. The remaining players are the skippers. Each skipper runs in, completes a number of jumps, and runs out, before the next skipper jumps in.

Game origins
Skipping is an excellent way to keep fit and is good training for athletes. These American children are performing a form of skipping called Double Dutch. This involves turning two ropes at the same time, and players require great concentration and coordination, as they jump both ropes.

HOPSCOTCH

Hopscotch, a game for any number of people, is played all over the world. There are many variations, but most hopscotch games involve hopping along a numbered board chalked on the ground and picking up stone counters.

You will need

Coloured chalk   *Stones*

Hopscotch board

The squares on this hopscotch board should be big enough to give you enough room to hop inside.

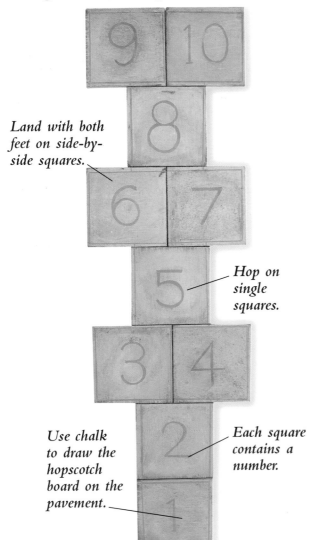

Land with both feet on side-by-side squares.

Hop on single squares.

Use chalk to draw the hopscotch board on the pavement.

Each square contains a number.

How to play

To make a hopscotch board, scratch the outline on firm dry earth, or draw it in chalk on a playground or pavement.

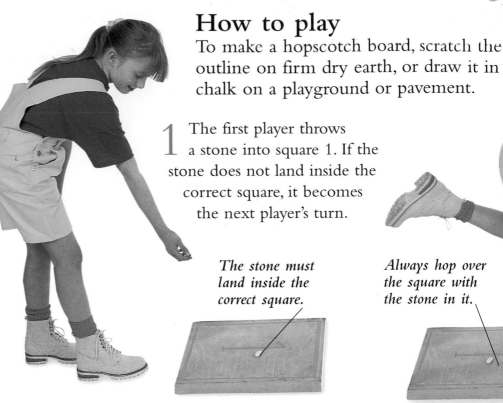

1 The first player throws a stone into square 1. If the stone does not land inside the correct square, it becomes the next player's turn.

The stone must land inside the correct square.

Always hop over the square with the stone in it.

5 If you lose your balance or throw the stone into the wrong square, it becomes the next player's turn. Start from the point where you went wrong when it's your turn again. The winner is the first player to complete the hopscotch up to square 10.

If one player overbalances, the next player takes a turn.

One foot lands on each side-by-side square.

2 Carefully hop over square 1 containing the stone and into square 2. Then continue down the board.

3 At the end of the board jump on numbers 9 and 10. Now jump around and return down the board to hop on to square 2.

Jump to face the other direction at the end.

4 Balancing on one foot in square 2, pick up the stone, then hop into square 1, and off the board. On each turn, throw the stone into the next square.

Pick up the stone on the return journey.

Jump over square 5 and into squares 6 and 7.

On the return trip, balance in square 6 and pick up the stone.

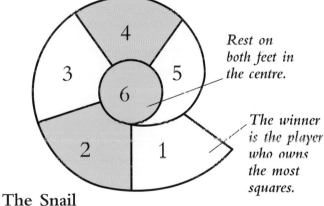

Alternative hopscotch games

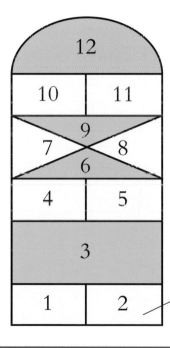

Rest on both feet in the centre.

The winner is the player who owns the most squares.

The Snail
A player hops to the centre of the board on one foot and back again. The player writes his or her name on a square. Only the owner can hop on to a named square. The game ends when all squares are owned and no one can hop to the centre.

The Pilgrim
A player kicks a stone into square 1 with his or her hopping foot, and hops into square 1. Then the player kicks the stone to square 2, then hops into square 2, and so on. A player whose foot or stone misses a square or touches a line is out.

Play continues in rounds until only one player remains.

When you reach the end of the board, jump around on both feet and hop back.

DROP THE HANKIE

Here's a simple game of bluff from India, called Dhamal Dhoko. By pretending to drop the hankie behind each player in a circle, you are creating an exciting guessing game. This game can be played indoors or out, with six or more players.

You will need

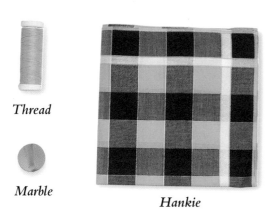

Thread

Marble

Hankie

EQUIPMENT

Scissors

Making the hankie

Cut off a length of thread. Place the marble in the centre of the handkerchief. Tie the thread securely around the marble, so it doesn't fall out.

How to play

To start the game, one player is chosen to be the bluffer. The rest of the players sit on the ground in a circle facing inwards.

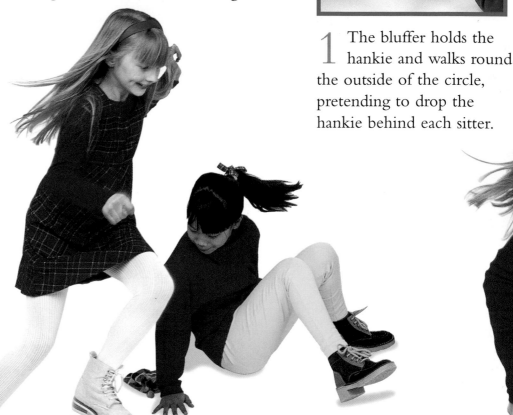

1 The bluffer holds the hankie and walks round the outside of the circle, pretending to drop the hankie behind each sitter.

2 When the hankie has been dropped, the bluffer carries on walking and bluffing, aiming to get right round the circle before the hankie has been discovered.

Game origins

With 800 million people living in India, there are many children to play drop the hankie, which is a simple way of entertaining large groups. The Taj Mahal, the symbol of India, was built for the Emperor's wife, who had a big family.

4 For the chaser to catch the bluffer, he or she must tap the bluffer on the back with the hankie. The chaser then returns to his or her space in the circle and the bluffer continues the game.

Chaser tapping the bluffer with the dropped hankie.

Double bluff
If the bluffer makes it around the circle undetected, the bluffer picks up the dropped hankie, taps the sitter with it on the back, and the two change places.

3 A sitter who feels the hankie behind them picks it up, and then chases the bluffer. The bluffer tries to escape the chaser by running round the circle and sitting down in the empty space before being caught.

The sitters are not allowed to look behind them to see if the hankie is there - they must feel for the hankie instead.

MANCALA

Mancala is a board game from Africa for two people, played by children and adults. It has many different names and rules. The board is sometimes made from wood, but is often just a series of holes scooped out of the ground. Placing the game pieces on the board is called "sowing". Beans, shells, or stones are traditionally used as game pieces, but you can use beads.

You will need

1 kg air-hardening modelling clay

Plain flour

Coloured paint

48 beads

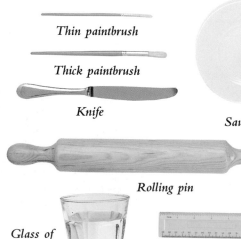

Tubes of all-purpose fabric paint★

EQUIPMENT

Thin paintbrush

Thick paintbrush

Knife

Saucer

Pepper pot

Rolling pin

Mug

Glass of water

Ruler

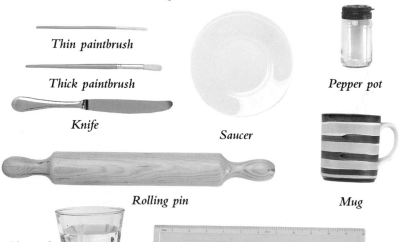

Making the board

1 Spread some plain flour on to a clean surface. Roll out the air-hardening modelling clay evenly with the rolling pin.

2 Cut a 50 cm x 10 cm board out of the clay. With the pepper pot, make 12 indents. Using the mug, put two indents at each end for stores.

3 Leave the clay board to harden and dry. Paint and decorate the board and paint one row of indents yellow and the other row red.

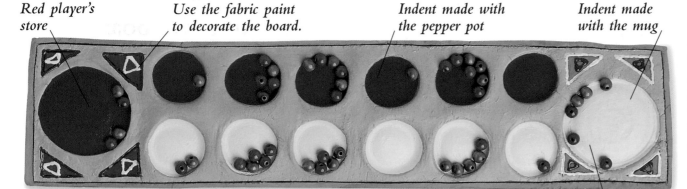

Red player's store

Use the fabric paint to decorate the board.

Indent made with the pepper pot

Indent made with the mug

Yellow player's store

Mancala board

The finished board is brightly coloured and has 6 indents or holes on each side with a store on each end, one for each player.

How to play

Each player starts with 24 beads. The object of the game is to capture the most beads.

Sowing one bead into each hole in an anti-clockwise direction

You can only take beads from the opponent's side.

1 Players sit either side of the board and put 4 beads in each hole on their row. Each player has an extra hole on their right to act as a store.

2 Each player scoops the beads out of any hole on his or her side and sows the beads one at a time into each hole anti-clockwise round the board.

3 If the last bead is dropped into an opponent's hole and the beads total 2 or 3, then the player scoops the beads up and puts them in the store.

4 If the hole immediately preceeding the now empty hole also has 2 or 3 beads, then the player may also take these beads. The game ends when a player has no beads left on his or her row. The winner is the player with the most beads in his or her store.

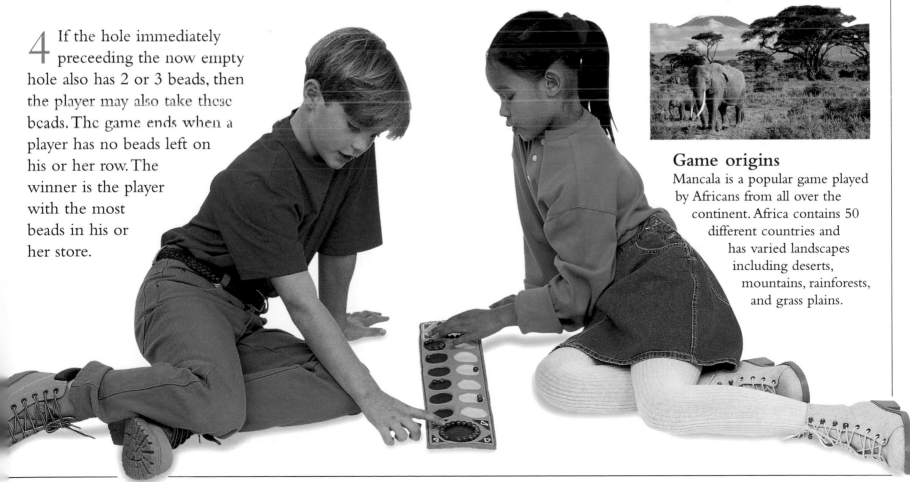

Game origins

Mancala is a popular game played by Africans from all over the continent. Africa contains 50 different countries and has varied landscapes including deserts, mountains, rainforests, and grass plains.

HYENA CHASE

This game for three or more players, comes from Sudan, a country in Central Africa that is mainly desert. Each circle on the game board represents a day's travel by the village women to reach a well in the desert to wash their clothes. The journey can be long, and in this game there is the added danger of being eaten by a hyena!

You will need

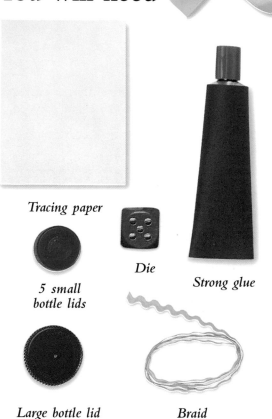

Tracing paper

5 small bottle lids

Die

Strong glue

Large bottle lid

Braid

Coloured ribbon

Coloured felt

EQUIPMENT

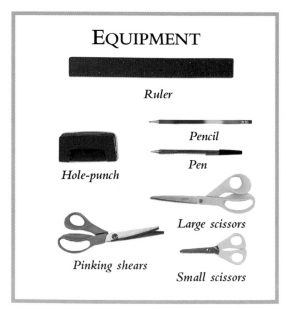

Ruler

Hole-punch

Pencil

Pen

Large scissors

Pinking shears

Small scissors

Making the game

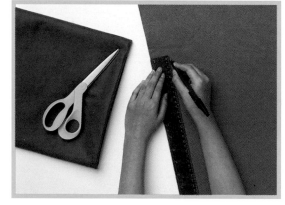

1 Measure and cut out some brown felt 50 cm x 50 cm. Cut four strips of green felt 50 cm long and glue to each edge. Decorate with braid.

2 Place a large bottle lid on a piece of beige felt. Draw around it 42 times and cut the circles out. Cut out small triangles for the arrows.

3 Glue the circles to the board in a spiral with the arrows in between. Cut out a hut, palm tree, and water jar and glue in place on the board.

4 Draw a hyena and four women's heads on tracing paper. Transfer these on to felt and cut out. Glue each head to a small lid for counters.

How to play

Players take turns to throw the die and travel to the well. They must return to the village before being eaten by the hyena!

Each circle represents a day's travel.

The village is the starting point

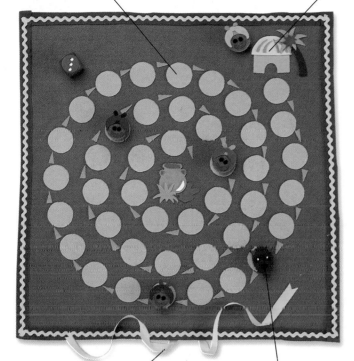

Roll the game up when finished and secure with ribbon.

Hyena counter

1 Players sit around the board and each chooses a village woman counter. Players must throw a 6 to begin their journey to the well.

2 Players take it in turns to throw the die and move their counters the number of circles indicated. A 6 gives a second go.

3 When players reach the well, they stop and wash their clothes. They cannot start the return journey until a 6 is thrown.

4 The first player back to the village is the winner, but the game is not over. This player then swaps the counter for the hyena.

5 The hyena travels to the well by moving twice the number shown on the die. When the hyena reaches the well, it drinks and returns to the village, eating up any counters it jumps over on the way.

Well

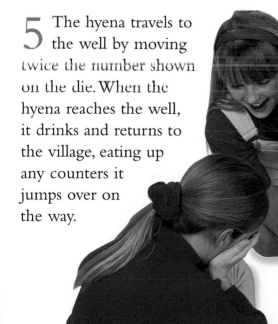

Hyena chasing the village women

Game origins

Sudan is the largest country in Africa. The nomadic peoples of this region travel with their camels and goats in search of food and water.

TRICKET

Tricket is a Colombian game of strategy for two players. Very similar to the game of Nine Men's Morris which originated in Iceland, Tricket has travelled across the world to South America.

You will need

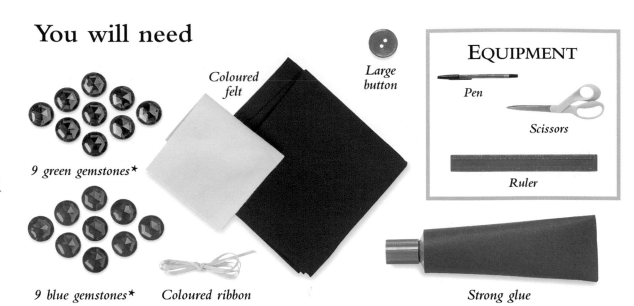

9 green gemstones★

9 blue gemstones★

Coloured felt

Large button

Coloured ribbon

EQUIPMENT

Pen

Scissors

Ruler

Strong glue

Making the board

1 Using a ruler, measure and draw with a pen a 36 cm x 36 cm square on a large piece of felt. Cut out the square to make the board.

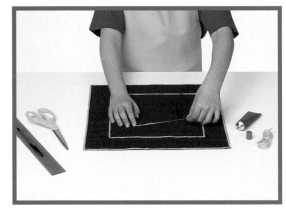

2 Inside the board, measure and draw two smaller squares. Glue thin ribbon around the board's edges and over the marked squares.

3 Glue more ribbon to connect the corners of each square. Then glue ribbon to connect the middles of each square's four sides, as shown.

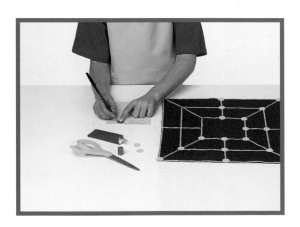

4 Trace around the button 24 times on a piece of felt. Cut out the felt circles and glue them to all the intersecting points on the board.

Tricket board

The tricket board is now ready to be played. The aim of the game is to form lines of three counters on the board.

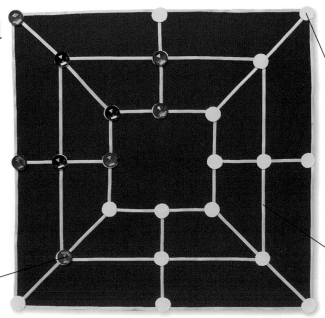

Corners are good strategic points to cover.

A grid of ribbon connects the points on the board.

Players place counters over the felt circles.

★Available from large department stores or craft shops.

Playing the game

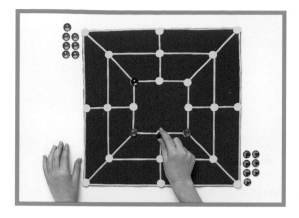

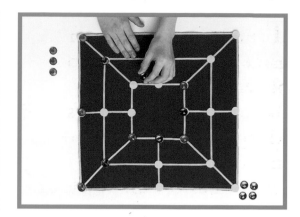

1 Each player has nine counters. The two players take it in turns to place their counters, one at a time, on any empty point on the board.

2 The object of the game is to form a line of three counters, all of the same colour, called a tricket. Try to block your opponent's trickets, as well.

3 When a player makes a line of three, he or she calls out 'tricket' and then removes any one of the other player's counters from the board.

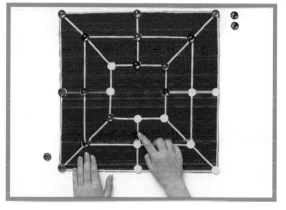

4 Once all of the counters have been placed on the board, the players move by sliding their counters to empty points on the board. A counter can only be moved to an adjoining point to the one it is on.

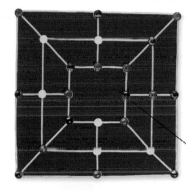

Blocking tactic
One way to win the game is to block your opponent's counters. This will leave your opponent without a point to move to.

The blue counters have blocked in the green counters.

Game origins
Spanish Conquistadores arrived in Colombia in the 16th century, bringing many new things from Europe, including their language and the game Tricket. The Conquistadores came to Colombia in search of local riches of gold and emeralds.

5 There are two ways to win tricket. You are the winner if the other player only has two counters left on the board. You can also win by blocking in your opponent.

A tricket can be formed horizontally, vertically, or diagonally.

COWS AND LEOPARDS

Cows and Leopards is a traditional board game from Sri Lanka. The game was played outside, and the board scratched into the ground using a stick. We have used coloured card for the board in this game for two players.

You will need

Coloured card

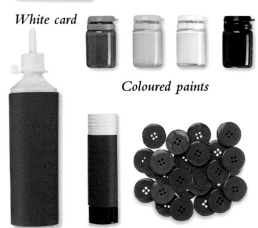

White card

Coloured paints

PVA glue   Glue stick   26 Buttons

EQUIPMENT

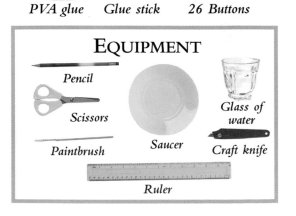

Pencil

Scissors

Paintbrush   Saucer   Craft knife

Glass of water

Ruler

Making the board

1 Cut out a piece of white card 40 cm x 40 cm. Draw a square 20 cm x 20 cm in the centre, and a triangle on each side, as shown.

2 Cut out of green card 32 triangles 4 x 4 x 5.5cm. Cut out eight triangles, 8 x 5 x 9 cm. Trim these in half widthwise to form two shapes.

3 Glue the 32 triangles on to the board within the drawn square. Leave a gap between each triangle. Fill the large triangles with the shapes.

4 Decorate the edges of the board with card to make it look like a jungle. Make sure that the card decorations fit around the game board.

Making the counters

5 Glue the pieces of card jungle to the board. Finally, cut 4 strips of blue card 40 cm long, and glue them down to the edge of the game board.

Paint two buttons yellow and leave to dry. Put on brown and orange spots for leopards. Paint 24 buttons white and let dry. Dab on brown spots for cattle.

How to play

1 One player has 24 cow counters and one has two leopards. To start, players take turns to put the pieces, one at a time, on any points of the board.

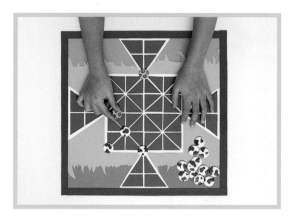

2 Once both leopards have been positioned, they may move along the lines in any direction including diagonally, one point at each turn.

3 The leopard can kill a cow by leaping over it on to a vacant point immediately beyond the cow. The cow is removed from the board.

4 Before they can move, all 24 cow counters must be placed. The aim for the cows is to pen the leopards into a corner of the board so they cannot move. The cows cannot jump over the leopards.

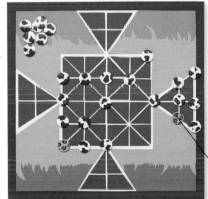

Penning in leopards
To prevent a leopard from moving, block all the points around the leopard with cow counters.

Penned in leopard

5 The player with the cow counters wins if he or she manages to pen in both leopards first. The leopards player wins if he or she removes all the cows.

Leopard leaping over the cow

Game origins
Sri Lanka is an island south of India, with many national parks. The spotted leopard is a protected animal and hunts mainly at night.

BEETLE GAME

There are many variations of the Beetle Game and it has been played for many years. It is a great party game to play for between two and six players. Make a beetle board for each player to use.

You will need

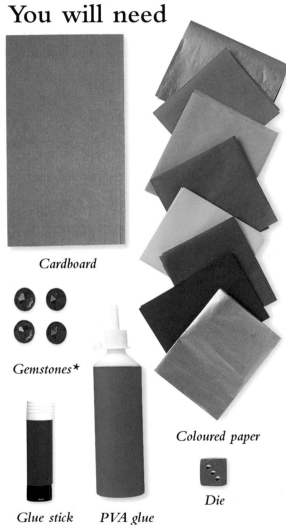

Cardboard

Gemstones*

Glue stick *PVA glue*

Coloured paper

Die

EQUIPMENT

Felt pen

Scissors

Thick paintbrush *Craft knife*

Making a beetle board

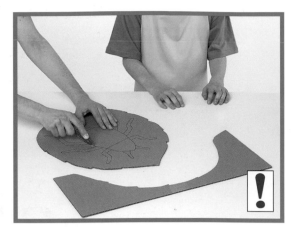

1 Draw a large leaf on a piece of cardboard. Inside the leaf, draw a beetle, with a body, head, six legs, two antennae, and a tail, as shown.

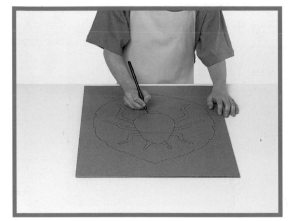

2 Ask an adult to cut the leaf out with the craft knife and then carefully cut out the body of the beetle, the legs, and antennae.

3 Push the legs and antennae out of the leaf. Using the scissors, carefully cut the head and the tail from the body, as shown.

4 To make eyes, trace around the gemstones on to the beetle head. Ask an adult to cut out the eye-holes with the craft knife.

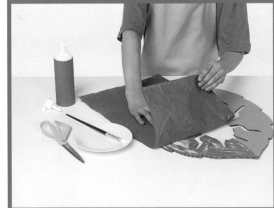

5 Brush glue on to the leaf and then cover each half with a sheet of coloured paper. Once the glue is dry, trim around the leaf.

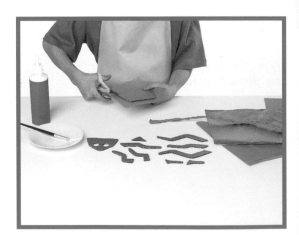

6 Cover the beetle in gold or silver paper. Trim any excess paper off the beetle. Decorate the beetle with twisted strips of paper.

Finished Beetle Game

The finished beetle pieces fit snugly into the leaf board. Each player selects a separate board. Start the game by pressing out the beetle parts.

How to play

Use different coloured paper for each player's board.

1 Each player must throw a 6 on the die to start. Once a player has thrown a 6, he or she can place the body in the leaf.

2 When the body is in place, the player throws the die and puts in the beetle body part represented by the number on the die.

3 After each throw, the next player has a turn. The player who completes their beetle first wins.

The eyes and antennae can only be placed on the beetle after the head is positioned.

Place the legs, eyes, and antennae one at a time.

If a player has the part represented on the die already on the board, then the turn passes to the next player.

Pieces of the beetle remaining to go on the leaf

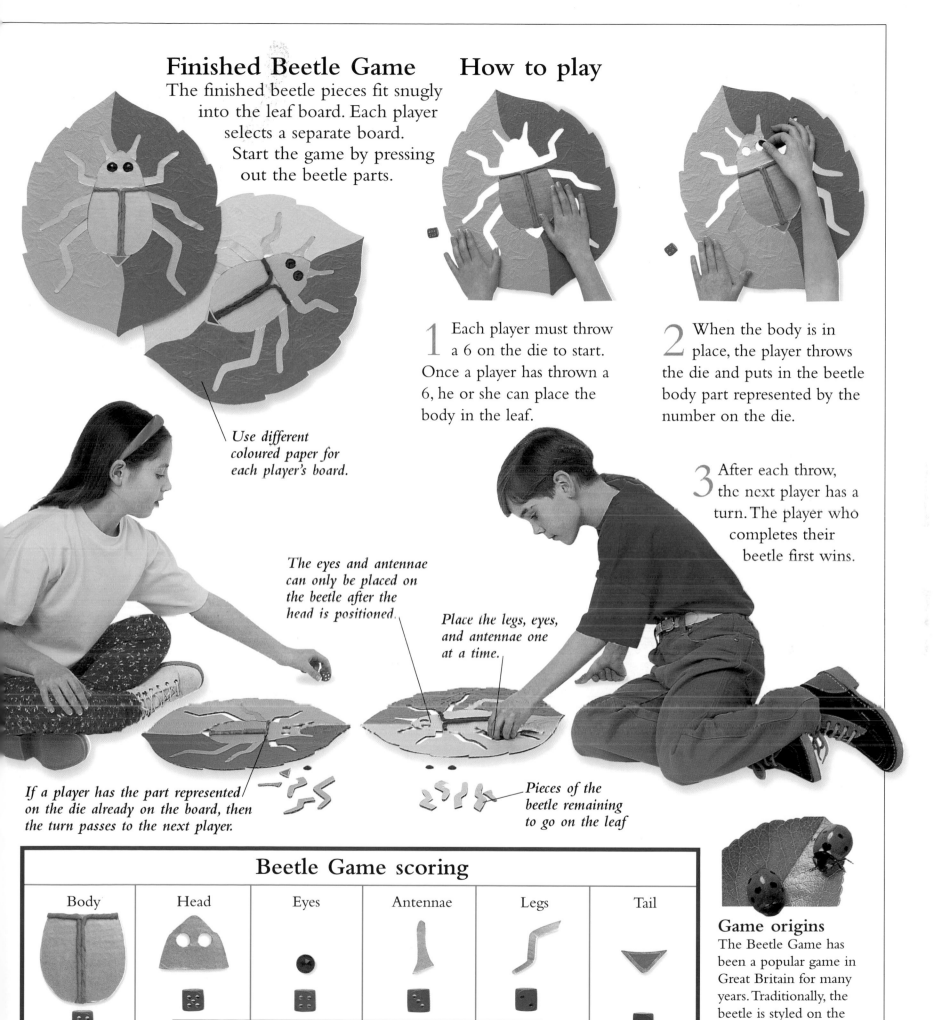

Beetle Game scoring

Body	Head	Eyes	Antennae	Legs	Tail

Each number on the die equals a beetle body part.

Game origins

The Beetle Game has been a popular game in Great Britain for many years. Traditionally, the beetle is styled on the ladybird and beetle parts are drawn on paper.

RACE GAMES

Here are some traditional games from around the world for any number of people to play at parties, in the garden, or in the playground.

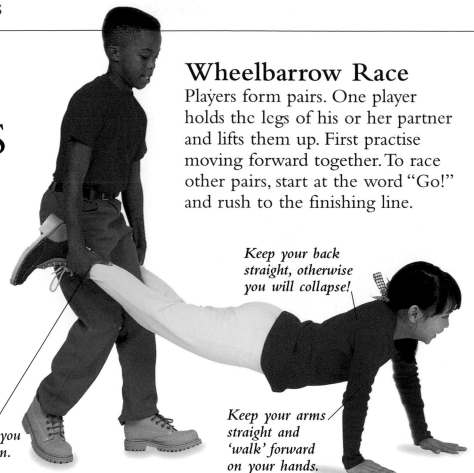

Wheelbarrow Race

Players form pairs. One player holds the legs of his or her partner and lifts them up. First practise moving forward together. To race other pairs, start at the word "Go!" and rush to the finishing line.

Keep your back straight, otherwise you will collapse!

Grip the legs firmly so that you don't drop them.

Keep your arms straight and 'walk' forward on your hands.

On the word "Go!", run up to the crouching player.

Sack Race

This game was originally played in potato sacks, but you can use old pillowcases instead. Each player steps inside a pillowcase and lines up at the race starting line and must hop to the finish.

You will need

A large pillowcase per person

The first player across the finishing line is the winner.

It is easy to fall over, so keep your balance by landing on both feet.

Hold the pillowcase firmly at the top.

On the word "Go!", each person has to hop to the finish.

Place a foot in each corner of the case.

Leapfrog Race

Players form pairs and decide how many leaps are in the race. One player in each pair runs five paces and crouches into a frog. The second player runs up, places his or her hands on the frog's back, and leaps over.

Continue the race
The second player then runs forward and crouches down into the frog position and the first player leaps over.

Keep your arms out for balance.

Place both hands firmly on the frog's back.

Keep your head well tucked in.

Bend down with your hands gripping your ankles.

The winners are the first players to complete the leaps.

Land safely and solidly with both feet apart.

The higher you leap, the further you will travel.

Hold on to the carrier's shoulders and sit on his or her hips.

On the word "Go!", the pairs run as fast as they can to the finishing line.

Hold on tight to the rider's legs.

Use a bag or cone as a finishing line marker.

Piggyback Race

Players form pairs. The lighter player climbs on to the stronger person's back and they line up at the start. If a pair collapses, they go back to the start.

CATTLE STOCKADE

Here's a game played by children in Botswana, a country in Africa. The name of the game comes from the 2.5 million cattle farmed in the country which are a very important source of food. Cattle Stockade is a rowdy game for six or more players that can be played indoors or out.

How to play

A group of four or more people link hands to form a fence or stockade and try to prevent the bull from escaping.

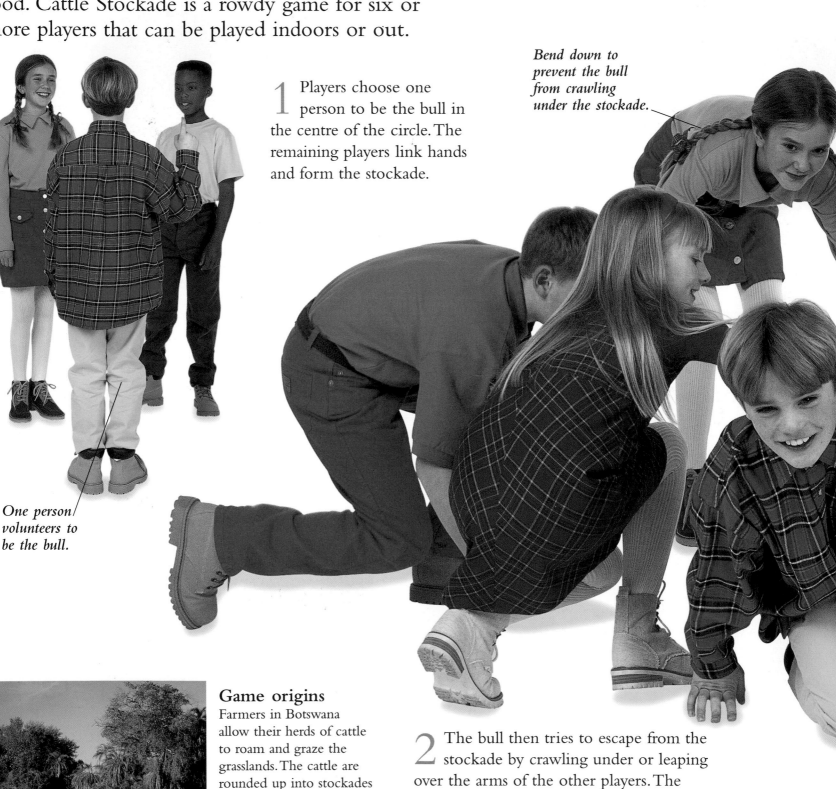

Bend down to prevent the bull from crawling under the stockade.

1 Players choose one person to be the bull in the centre of the circle. The remaining players link hands and form the stockade.

One person volunteers to be the bull.

Game origins

Farmers in Botswana allow their herds of cattle to roam and graze the grasslands. The cattle are rounded up into stockades when they need to be branded or sold.

2 The bull then tries to escape from the stockade by crawling under or leaping over the arms of the other players. The stockade try to stop the bull escaping, without letting go of each other's hands.

Linking hands
To form a strong stockade, players should link hands tightly, as shown.

Cattle stampede!
A large group of players can make the game more challenging by adding more cattle to the stockade.

3 Once the bull has escaped, he or she can join the stockade and choose another player to be the bull.

Another way for the bull to escape is stepping over the linked arms of the stockade.

The bull tries to escape the stockade.

INDEX